Positivity, Beauty & Self Love

In Dedication to my family and friends, who always support my craziness and stand by me without judgement. It's you who help make my journey very interesting. I am full of life because of you.
You all know who you are.
Love you.. too much..too much..
Julia♥ ✿

Written By Julia A. Rosenberg
Cover Design and Photography By Hannah M. Rosenberg

CONGRATULATIONS !!

You have taken the first step in investing in you. I am so excited for you because it is such a great feeling knowing that with bits and pieces from this book and the things I'll talk to you about mixed with your own experiences, You will be able to get through your days easier and so much more relaxed and organized. Change things up and you can't miss. Take the extra step. You've already made the first move.

First, i'm going to get you a little more acquainted with me so you can have a better idea of who is talking to you. You've seen my picture on the back cover, that's me. Julia. Jules. Julie. I pretty much

answer to any of those. I'm 53 years old. I'm a high

school grad with some college but stopped college

½ way through and went to work full time so I could

help my family. *(sometimes you don't have a*

choice, It's all good though, I've had a great life

even with all the bumps.) I have 3 really great

children that I've been graced with, although they

are not babies anymore, I am so very involved in

what's going on with them, I feel you have to be. I

am blessed with my beautiful 84 year old mom who

is healthy and amazing. I have been married twice,

to two amazing men. First time for 6 years and the

2

second time for 20 years. My 2 ex husbands are

both very big parts of my life and I wouldn't trade

my crazy modern family for the world. I am 3 years

new to being a homeowner. I know we are all

pushing through life and I believe I have finally

figured some things out and I wanted to share.

HERE WE GO …

SELF ENHANCEMENT

With this pandemic, most of us found ourselves

with so much time that we didn't know

what to do with, but we figured it out. We enjoyed

much needed family time and turned

the clocks back to years ago where we didn't have

social media or cell phones. We

played games and did crafts and puzzles that the

the whole family worked on.

Family breakfast, lunch and dinners took place. I

cannot count how many meals I made in the last

few months, taking care of everyone, I lost myself

in the process, so it was a great thing for my family

and a neglect of the self care thing for me. I was so

involved in precious family time, I didn't want to

miss a second. Time was appreciated.

Now that we are on a cycle of the world getting

back to somewhat normal (*whatever*

that is) We should get our body, mind, and soul

back to basics. We are all going back to

work and everything is opening up and taking care

of you is the first step.

Starting by taking part of your day for you. Taking

that extra ½ hour in the morning and at night added

to the regular time you already use.

Throwing a little pampering into yourself, really

makes so much of a difference in your

day and in the way you carry yourself through the

day.

My morning routine consists of a cup of whatever

morning beverage I feel like having

that day, a small workout, a light stretch, a shower

and makeup routine. Clothes picked

out the night before really helps keeping the stress

level of wondering what to wear in

the morning. It saves time and reduces stress. It

one hundred percent allows you to

start your day in a good mood.

During your day, embrace the things that make you

different. The world needs your differences,

whatever makes you stand above the crowd. Think

about it. We are not all the same and our

differences, the way we look at things, and the way

we go about leading our lives will make a huge

impact if you just embrace yourself.

Self Love

Time for you sounds very easy. What even is that?

Who has the time? Ok, there are 24

hours in a day. Realistically, 4-6 hours of that is

spent sleeping. *(I haven't had a good*

night's sleep in 20 years) That leaves

approximately 18 hours. With that, 8-9 hours is

spent working. Whether it's around the house with

the kids or at a job.

That leaves 9 hours. A combination of 3 hours is

spent in meal prep or figuring out what

to eat, 3 hours doing errands, 2 hours cleaning or

being lazy, and with your last hour,

Well, that is spent split, ½ hour of self morning

prep and ½ hour bedtime prep.

There you go, the typical way 24 hours is spent.

Again I ask, Who has extra time?

Well, I will tell you, ME . I have extra time and I will

tell you why. Job, children, daily things that come

up, doctors, occasions to go to, meetings, they are all important, YES I agree, but you can take care of all that and have time for you first. Realizing that is the beginning of making self love work for you.

I see way too many posts on social media about so many different self quotes.Some quotes are about being strong, some say stay away from toxic people, some say :

This is a lesson or knowing the truth but believing the lies, some talk about always putting your kids first no matter what.

 My favorite is :

I am a new person and I am a strong woman.

Well, yes these quotes all help for the moment they are being posted so the person posting is getting self gratification, but it's only temporary. And

The reason why it's temporary is very simple.

All these quotes are plain Bullshit if you do not put an action behind the words.

Mind blowing right? So simple you would think but 9 out of 10 people do not put actions

behind their words when it comes to quotes. They just say or post the quote to get

temporary satisfaction. And that is fine but by doing that you are not exercising self love.

This is my quote that I like : I am strong and

confident and I am self supportive.

This is my action that I just recently figured out, just

so you know, it is never too late to

start. My action: Eating right, meditation to cleanse

the mind, and educate others to do

The same: hence this book.

Have you ever heard this saying? If you do not

love yourself, no one else will.

Well, I think that is not exactly true. I think I will take

my VETO stamp and stamp out the

Negativity on that statement. I am so sure that what

they meant to say is that by loving

yourself, your mind and body develop a self

empowerment strong enough so you can

be confident around others, because of that, others

will see you differently. (FACT)

TIME MANAGEMENT

Make a list. It's simple, it's just an outline of your

day. Every day every list is different.

My days vary, keeping it interesting especially

during this pandemic where the gyms

Were closed and I couldn't go. But some mornings,

I rode my bike or I chose to walk or

sat and enjoyed the morning sun. Of course it was

easier to switch things up during the

pandemic when everything was closed and you

couldn't work or do errands. But still,

those moments of mini time breaks were not

enough for me, the level of self love that

my body and mind needed is usually three times

what I was taking for myself during the

pandemic giving myself to the entire family, keeping

them sane and somewhat

entertained I experienced some self neglect

because my body and mind wasn't getting

the self love that I was used to. I realized that Self

love is so important and giving time

to yourself is the biggest gift ever.

Let's continue with some of the ways that self love

completes us.

Cell Phones- What do cell phones have to do with self love? Well, replace an hour a day from using social media from your cell phone with listening to music or calling someone you haven't spoken to in a long time just to hear their voice, or meditation or write an actual letter on paper and mail it to a long time friend or someone special in your life. (*One time I received a card from a friend in the mail with beautiful things written in it and I was elated for days, even now when I think of my snail mail treat , I smile*)

Or for that very busy person, use that time to do

something that you wouldn't normally

do like a detox mask or read a book. I have to tell

you when the books came out that

what seemed like the whole world read, Fifty

Shades of Grey by E.L.James in 2011

Everyone gave themselves self love. People that

never read before stopped what they

were doing and reading every book. They filled

their days reading. It was an eye opener

for most people. They found the time in their busy

schedules to read. It was such a

beautiful thing that people are destressing by

reading.

Although social media is important in this day and

age, we need to take time away from it

to get back what we are missing.

At a job that I had prior to the pandemic the

employees used their cell phones on a

regular basis. Actually no cell phones was one of

the rules. No matter what the

management did, it didn't matter. Productivity was

down and this was part of the

reason. If one person looks at their phone a max of

20 times a day for only 45 seconds

at a time, that is 15 minutes. With 40 employees

doing this at 15 min each, that is a

total of 10 hours,That is the total of time not spent

moving product. That was 10 hours of

company time looking at cell phones checking

social media. Thats crazy. This is for

one day. That's 70 hours a week not being

productive. These people were consumed

with social media. Wake up people. Social media is

taking your day away from self

loving yourself. From getting things accomplished

to doing something for yourself.

I'm not nor will I ever say stop using social media

because it is also important, but what I am saying

is, Curb your time on the Social scene and you will

have the time to get things done and you will have so much less stress and that is the base of

self love.

LAUGHING AT YOURSELF

Crazy right ? I thought so too. But I have a

friend,(*one of my besties by the way*),

who laughs at herself all the time. We will be in the

car or out somewhere or even on

the phone and she will say something to me and

then laugh at it.

Like it's so funny. (*and it usually is*) But she laughs

at her own

statement or joke. There have been times she cant

even finish what she was saying

because in her head she knows what she is saying

and it's so funny she already started

laughing. I used to think she was completely nuts.

But now, I believe she is genius. She

is relieving her stress through laughter. That's right

folks, it equals self love. She knows

in her heart that laughter is connected to a person's

well being, their sanity. She is

without realizing it, cleansing her soul with laughter.

I just absolutely admire that so

much. Maybe we don't laugh at ourselves enough

in life. We definitely don't.

It's proven that Laughter is a healthy way to relieve stress. It releases Neuropeptides that are beneficial to your immune system. Just like working out releases endorphins which also is like taking a happy pill.

In an internet article written by the Mayo Clinic Staff, Some of the short term benefits of laughter are not limited to but do include : stimulating many organs, activating and relieving stress response, soothing tension. Not to mention the long term effects by improving immune system, relieving pain and some interesting

Other facts that laughter does to benefit your well

being. The Mayo Clinic staff goes into more detail in their article. Definitely look it up, it's a great read.

Our days consist of 24 hours, and on that day there are 1440 minutes. I am positive that in 1440 minutes we do something that is so stupid we get angry at ourselves. Instead of getting angry, What do we have to do? That's right. Laugh at it. Laughing cleanses and anger causes stress. I'd rather be known as the person who laughed it off instead of the person who got mad all the time.

Self Love is my favorite thing to talk about because

treating yourself with love and care

is the greatest thing you can do for yourself. Some

things you can start with is meditation, candles,

shopping sprees, take a break, vacations. It doesn't

have to be far away or on a plane somewhere to be

a vacation. It could be as easy as two towns over

go apple picking, stroll through the sunflower farms,

have a great dinner and stay at a

hotel and come home the next day or evening.

Taking a break from your daily grind or

routine with family members, friends or alone,

whatever works for you.

What else do you think you can add to your day to

lessen your day? If you think that is a

crazy question, it is. It is crazy. You might ask, How

can you lessen your day by adding

things to do without adding time but by adding

things to do? The answer is by adding

your extra things, the things you love will lessen

your stress and you will easily get the

things in your day done because you will be

relaxed, calm and focused. Whatever you

need to do to relax, add it to your day. Whether its,

lighting candles, playing music,

shopping, getting away now and then, crafts,

painting, planting, baking, playing with or

training your pet, or washing your car. Whatever it

is, add it to your day and your well

being will allow you to get everything done.

Today I had a list to do, bank, post office ,

supermarket. Well, normally, I'd get up, do my

morning preparation and then go do my errands

and in my day I'd have to somehow fit

these things in. But before I went to bed, my

daughter asked me to bring her to school

in the morning. Now, being divorced and the fact

that my daughter is some days with

me and some days with her dad. This particular day

she was at her dads in the morning

and taking her was an extra step but of course

doable. So I had to set my alarm a little

earlier and completely be done for my day before I

left the house to get her for school. I

loved my extra morning with my sweet girl and

although this was an added extra thing, I

was so wonderfully happy and relaxed because I

just got some precious time with her. A

non split family always has all their kids all the time

but when the time is shared, you

realize how precious it is.

I took her to school and got all my errands done in

record time and still had extra time to

do some things off of my tomorrow list. And all

because when I got the call to take my

daughter to school, instead of hanging up and

dealing with it in the morning, and

running around chasing time in the morning like a

crazy person, I made a list, set my

alarm a little earlier and because I love myself

enough to take the time to prep my day

so I'm not a mess, I also got my clothes ready and

made a shopping list. Then I did my

night prep and went to bed.

Daily lists

Organization of time is easier than you think. To start all you have to do is get yourself a notebook. One subject is fine, I find that time management is key, so I use the "by time" method. But some people use the "by date" method. Of course getting a planner is a great idea to keep track of certain dates, the notebook is for your daily lists. You can even find a notebook that fits right in your planner. Whatever works for you, it's a preference thing but I suggest that you pick one because winging it will just stress you out in the long run. Just so you know, I'm sharing

these things out of experience.

50 years of stressed out experience, some fun and

some not so fun and always either way

too early to things or way too late, never on time

and always not getting to everything I

had to do on that day. Finally after 3 years of

practicing time management successfully, I

figured out that Positivity, Beauty, and Self Love

really adds quality to your life. Time to

start. Make a List.

DAILY LIST

By Time:

Example:

Sunday September 20, 2020

7:00am_____
_____

7:30am_____
_____

8:00am_____
_____

8:30am_____
_____

9:00am_____
_____

9:30am_____
_____

10:00am_____
_____

10:30am_____

Etc. continue all the way to 10 pm
By Date:

Example:

Sunday September 20,2020

_____
_____
_____
_____
_____
_____
_____
_____
_____
_____
_____
_____
_____
_____
_____
_____
_____
_____
_____

You will see that everything we talk about starts

with a list. Inorder to make things work,

it is critical that you start with a list. Like an outline

almost but so you have a daily plan, I

am certain that's why they call it a planner.You

should also have a long time plan as

well, one that you know you want like adding things

to your house or things you want to

buy or things you want to do or places to go. Maybe

it's that you aren't financially ready

for these things yet or the time isn't right. Whatever

it is, at least you will be ready and

focused when the time comes.

FINANCES

Time to get those finances in order. Get a book,

one you will only use for this.

Preferably, one that the pages don't rip out.

List all your Bills, finances, creditors, anyone you

pay on a monthly basis. Give each

creditor a page and on each page list all the login

information. Because whether you

have it come out automatically or do it manually,

you should always list it and keep

track. Write the months down and everytime a

payment is made, just check it off or put

the confirmation number down. By doing this, you

will have some idea of your debt,

what you have coming in and what is going out.

This will absolutely help eliminate stress.

On each page every creditor gets their <u>own page.</u>

EXAMPLE:

Mortgage: My home mortgage company Acct#
XXXXXXX Payment amt: XXXX.XX
Due date: first every month Phone #
XXX-XXX-XXXX

2020

Jan : Paid XXXX.XX on 1/1/2020 Conf#
XXXXXXXX
Feb: Paid XXXX.XX on 2/1/2020 Conf#
XXXXXXXX
Mar:
April:
May:
June:
July:
Aug:
Sept:
Oct.:
Nov:
Dec:

In a different part of the book maybe last 12 pages

one for each month. Make a list of all

your income from all sources in one section and the

total amount to be paid out, this will

keep you on track and clear headed.

Example:

January 2020

Paychecks 3rd, 10th, 17th, 24th, 31st each check $ 850.
Babysitting 16th, 19th, 24th   each day $ 60.

Total month income : $ 4430.
 Automatically put 10% of income in savings: $ 443.
Bills, creditors including gas, food : $ 3750.
That leaves a balance of $ 237 misc for the month
for you.

Now keep in mind that your bills will include your

extra curricular activities like going out

with friends, gas in car, food, all creditors etc. the

balance is yours for anything that

comes up and if you do not use it then it rolls over

to the next month. Also keep in mind

that it is very important to treat your savings like a

creditor so if you have a cushion.

This is a very big part in keeping yourself stress

free or low stress because you will be

clear headed and able to have functionality.

BEAUTY

Beauty is inside all of us. Every Race, every size

person, every gender in our own way.

We all have beauty. It is not in the way you look,
the

clothes that you wear, where you

live, or what you drive. Beauty is you. It's how you

see yourself and how you treat

yourself and others.

There are several definitions of beauty.

 One is: The best feature or advantage of

something.

Another is: A combination of qualities that pleases

the intellect or moral sense.

Now, with that being said, feeling beautiful or good about yourself comes from within and to do that, it starts with a good healthy eating habit and exercise. I do not have to be a doctor to tell you that healthy eating habits are for sure the key to feeling good.

But of course Always check with your doctor first to help determine the plan that is best for you. When you feel good, everything the way you live your life, improves.

A life coach or trainer will always head you in the right direction for an exercise routine that is fit for your body. Whether you are looking to lose weight or you are looking to just

live your life on a healthier path, make sure to get

your check up first to start your

internal beauty journey. I have Ulcerative Colitis

and I take medicine to regulate my

issues. In turn I also eat a Gluten free diet because

it helps me digest easier. And being

Gluten free for years, my system has no tolerance

for gluten. My doctor gave me the

green light for a workout program that I started with

a trainer, Mike and he is certified in

body training and development and Physical

Therapy and he put me on a path to have

a great workout routine that after many years with

him , I now do without him but am

very grateful for his training and knowledge.
Thanks Mike.

I totally believe in Skincare. I am a certified Beauty

Advisor trainer. I know that even if

you do not wear makeup, a good skincare routine is

so very important in keeping your

skin healthy. Find an affordable skincare product

line that fits your budget and with just a

few products your skin will thank you with a natural

glow and elasticity that it should

have. An eye cream, a day cream or lotion and a

night cream are your three main

products. There are other products, so many others

but if you are on a budget, these

three are the products you should have.

Face masks are always a good idea and they are

for sale at every price point. The relaxing feeling

that a face mask brings is wonderful. It's

not like you can walk around for the ½

hour that the mask is placed on your face unless

you use a spread on mask. But, if you

are using the lay on face mask, Use this time to

relax, unwind and recharge. Light some

candles, play some music or just close your eyes.

Nothing beats that feeling.

I Love, Love, Love it.

Home Remedies

There are so many Homeopathic remedies for skin

care. Foods from your own kitchen

are at your fingertips.

Cucumber is an oldie but a goodie. You always

see cucumber slices on the eyelids of

someone getting a facial or relaxing on television.

You might think food on the face is

funny, it kind of is, but it's also true. Cucumbers are

hydrating and they give your skin

nourishment that is very good for your skin. You

can lay slices on your eyes or blend in

the blender for a paste to place on your face.

Coconut oil is one natural ingredient that you can

use. Warm oil with your hands and

apply to your face and neck for 7-9 minutes then

rinse off, use once a day.

Baking Soda, **Lemon, and Water** makes a great

paste that will exfoliate your skin. Rub

all over then rinse. And do this a few times a week.

 So as you can see there are regular

foods that you can use that I am sure

will help instead of purchasing all kinds of products.

I will list some foods and what they

are good for that I have learned from experience

and my extensive training in this field,

but of course and I reiterate, always check with

your doctor. If you have any allergies to

certain foods, do not apply those foods to your

face. You will without a doubt have an

allergic reaction. Example: If you are Gluten Free,

you can not use flour or wheat based ingredients

on your skin.

If you are allergic to nuts, Of course do not use any

ingredients with nuts, same applies to citrus or any

other food.

Please pay close attention to the ingredients !

Here are some at home remedies with regular food
for skin care recipes that you can try. Do your
research on the quantities. You can find
many websites that have part for part for the
measures and usage on how many
times per week and how long to leave on.

Cucumbers: Hydration for skin

Baking Soda: Balances the PH in your skin, To
help keep it clear, whitens teeth.

Aloe: kills acne bacteria , soothes skin, and
moisturizes.

Honey: Moisturizes

Turmeric: skin lightener

Lemon: removes dead cells, promotes clear skin

Green apple: helps minimizes wrinkles

Tomato and Lime: reduces dark circles

Sour Cream, Banana, Honey: helps keep natural glow to skin

Puree Papaya: Lightens freckles and blemishes

Castor oil and eggs: Hair mask

Vitamin E, Witch Hazel, Olive oil, water: make up remover

Basil: toner

There are so many more, use the internet for part

for part and usage instructions.

Listed above are a few that I have used and love.

If you are doing something for yourself then beauty

will be your result. It's all about

changes or doing extra things in your day added to

your regular routine to reduce stress

levels and enhance your day.

Age Gracefully- It is in your hands. You have the

power to change your life.

POSITIVITY

So in each Chapter I spoke to you about so many

different things, but on every topic, I

mentioned lists and how important they are and

that they are the root of your success in

everything you do.The importance of lists is beyond

what I can express. Making daily

lists will help you with Self love, Beauty, and

Positivity.

HOW DOES SOCIAL MEDIA TAKE PART ?

How many of you are on social media? My guess

is going to be almost all of you.

So, you wake up and grab your phone and check

what is going on with friends, acquaintances, and

family. You send birthday wishes and have political

arguments and even post about your day. I know

this because I do it too. Cyber world plays a big

part in our lives. When I go on in the morning, I

always start with a bit of positivity. Maybe I

will say good morning, have a beautiful day or

enjoy your day, or something of that

nature. It makes me feel so good and I think it is

because I want to feel good and I want

everyone else to feel the same. Although it's

generic on social media, it's not without

feeling. Seeing all the people that you touch when

you do that is the best feeling. It

definitely helps to start the day. Keeping things

positive no matter how many obstacles

are in your way pointing things to negative is hard

to do but if you train yourself to turn

on your override switch. YOU have the power to

override it . Override the negativity.

Remember the VETO stamp? Well, Veto negativity!

Staying positive will change your

outlook on life, reduce stress and add to you loving

you.

MANIFEST

Manifest what you want and stay positive. Using

and understanding crystals are a great

way to keep yourself positive. And Being a spiritual

person I understand crystals and I

know that they magnify the manifestation. Using

crystals for manifestation is easy and

helps you feel empowered. You can purchase

crystals of all kinds in crystal stores or

online. Crystals have different energies.

Tigers Eye: This stone/Crystal is a healing stone

for relieving doubt and gives you the energy of

clarity and strength.

Clear Quartz: this crystal is a magnifier , it

amplifies the other crystals strengths, On its own, It

attracts balance and good health.

Rose Quartz : One of my fave crystals. The Love

crystal. It opens you to Love, to accepting and

giving Love. So many have also believed it to help fertility.

Citrine: Attracts wealth, money and success. It increases creativity. It clears out negativity and brings Calm.

Amethyst: Helps connect with your hidden feelings, this stone works to purify any space of negative vibrations.

Sodalite: This crystal is a great way to bring harmonizing energy to yourself when you need it, It helps you find the words and the confidence to communicate clearer.

Sodalite stimulates endurance, and if you are public speaking or performing in art or a sport, or writing.

Hematite: Grounds and balances you. Calming, absorbs negative energy. It centers you with a subtle calming effect.

There are so many others and I could go on for pages, but these are a few of my favorites. Now that I explained what some of the crystals do, How do we incorporate manifesting what you want and keeping positivity and crystals?

Well Holding your preferred crystal asking the universe for your wants, manifests it to become a reality. Picture it. Be clear in your head. For example: if it's that job you want, or promotion.

Pick your crystals you chose to use,

picture yourself there with that job, in that position

and almost like a wish but really see

yourself there, keep it positive. Then you have to

list the steps that you need to take to

achieve your goals to physically put yourself there.

Work toward your goals and keep

your crystals on your person, wear them or pocket

them but they will give you the

energy that you need and the confidence to get

there. Some might say that this is fake

but being spiritual I can tell you that it is not fake. It

is in fact, very real. Just like the

followers of different religions choose to believe

certain things and pray in their own

ways. I stand by all of those followers because they

believe in something that they

cannot see, but they feel. Spiritual people like

myself, believe in the power of positivity,

the healing powers of crystals and manifestation

and the strength and guidance of the Universe.

Positive Acts always keep your goals positive and

achievable.

KEEPING A JOURNAL

Keeping a journal is a great way to write down your

daily activities and milestones,

anything you want to remember. The events,

feelings, anything that happened in your

day and recording in writing the memory. By doing

this, it keeps your mind clear and it

relieves stress and also keeps you positive. It's an

outlet. I love keeping a journal. It

keeps me peaceful. To be honest, sometimes I

forget to write in it at night then I'll pick it

up in the middle of the day to fill in my thoughts or

happenings. But there have been

times I didn't write my thoughts for a few days and

then I just pick it up out of nowhere

and do some writing. Do you know what's the best

part? The best part is, It's YOUR

journal and no one will see it, no one will get mad at

you for skipping days. So use it as

your outlet. No one is judging you. Someone told

me once that your opinion is your

opinion and no one can tell you that it's wrong

because it's yours. Well, the same rule

applies to your journal. It's yours and no one will

ever tell you that it's wrong the way you

write in it or what you say. Your outlet is yours and

only yours. Keep it real. Keep your head clear.

During my house construction, in the middle of a

pandemic, having no job and every

interview being postponed because of a hiring

freeze, can't go out, petrified to get sick

and having no insurance, losing my step dad,

keeping my 84 year old mom and kids

safe. It was pretty hard to keep positive as most of

the world felt too. But between my

journal, my lists, my crystals, and my devotional

that I read daily. I got through one of

the roughest times with a positive outlook.

A devotional is a great way to get a quote or

scripture. There are devotionals with a

daily read on every page with quotes of

inspirational reads in every religion, spiritual

essence, and just some that are fun and happy

quotes. As you can probably tell, I am

not an extremely religious person but I am spiritual

and I believe Beauty , Positivity and

Self Love are the Key drivers in the reason I

couldn't possibly love myself any more

than I already do.

I always joke and tell people that the more positive I

may seem to them, The worse my day is going. But

that's how I deal with some issues. I try to see the

light in the darkness. My favorite saying is: "When

life gives you lemons, then make lemonade."

(But I believe that when the most refreshing drink of

lemonade does not do the trick, then

add vodka.)

All of us are the same on the inside. We are all

women and men, we are all sizes , shapes, and

races. We were all born, we all Live, Love, Laugh

and Cry. We all bleed only one color, RED.

Stop the hate

………. Breed the Positivity, Beauty, and Self Love

OK so now you have the next

25 pages to use.

Make your lists, start right here

until you can get the supplies

you need.

The NEXT 25 pages are BLANK

*Write your story, start your
lists, or journals…
Why wait ?   Start Now ..
       You got this life thing…*

Daily Lists or Journal

_____

_____

_____

_____

_____

_____

_____

_____

_____

_____

_____

_____

_____

_____

_____

_____

_____

_____

_____

_____

_____

_____

_____

_____

_____

_____

Daily Lists or Journal

_____

_____

_____

_____

_____

_____

_____

_____

_____

_____

_____

_____

_____

_____

_____

_____

_____

_____

_____

_____

_____

_____

Daily Lists or Journal

Daily Lists or
Journal

Daily Lists or
Journal

_____

_____

_____

Daily Lists or

*Journal*_____

_____

_____

_____

_____

_____

_____

_____

_____

_____

_____

_____

_____

_____

_____

_____

_____

_____

_____

_____

Daily Lists or
Journal

Daily Lists or
Journal

Daily Lists or
Journal

_____

_____

_____

Daily Lists or

_Journal_____

_____

_____

_____

_____

_____

_____

_____

_____

_____

_____

_____

_____

_____

_____

_____

_____

_____

_____

_____

_____

_____

_____

Daily Lists or

*Journal*_____

_____

_____

_____

_____

_____

_____

_____

_____

_____

_____

_____

_____

_____

_____

_____

_____

_____

_____

_____

_____

_____

_____

Daily Lists or
*Journal*_____

_____

_____

_____

_____

_____

_____

_____

_____

_____

_____

_____

_____

_____

_____

_____

_____

_____

_____

_____

_____

Daily Lists or
Journal

Daily Lists or

Journal

_____

_____

_____

Daily Lists or

*Journal*_____

_____

_____

_____

_____

_____

_____

_____

_____

_____

_____

_____

_____

_____

_____

_____

_____

_____

_____

_____
_____
_____

Daily Lists or
*Journal*_____

_____
_____
_____
_____
_____
_____
_____
_____
_____
_____
_____
_____
_____
_____
_____
_____
_____
_____
_____
_____
_____
_____
_____

_____

_____

_____

Daily Lists or

*Journal*_____

_____

_____

_____

_____

_____

_____

_____

_____

_____

_____

_____

_____

_____

_____

_____

_____

_____

_____

_____

_____

_____

Daily Lists or
*Journal*_____

_____

_____

_____

_____

_____

_____

_____

_____

_____

_____

_____

_____

_____

_____

_____

_____

_____

_____

_____

_____

_____

_____

Daily Lists or

_Journal_____

_____

_____

_____

_____

_____

_____

_____

_____

_____

_____

_____

_____

_____

_____

_____

_____

_____

_____

_____

_____

_____

Daily Lists or

_Journal_____

_____

_____

_____

_____

_____

_____

_____

_____

_____

_____

_____

_____

_____

_____

_____

_____

_____

_____

_____

_____

_____

_____

Daiy Lists or
_Journal_____

_____

_____

_____

_____

_____

_____

_____

_____

_____

_____

_____

_____

_____

_____

_____

_____

_____

_____

_____

_____

Daily Lists or
Journal

Daily Lists or
Journal

_____

_____

_____

Daily Lists or

_Journal_____

_____

_____

_____

_____

_____

_____

_____

_____

_____

_____

_____

_____

_____

_____

_____

_____

_____

_____

_____

Daily Lists or

*Journal*_____

_____

_____

_____

_____

_____

_____

_____

_____

_____

_____

_____

_____

_____

_____

_____

_____

_____

_____

_____

Made in the USA
Middletown, DE
30 October 2020